MW00605574

THE TYRANNY OF DATA

Arthur Getis

Tenth University Research Lecture
San Diego State University

Graduate Division and Research

SAN DIEGO STATE UNIVERSITY PRESS

Copyright © 1995 by
San Diego State University Press

All rights reserved.

Except for brief passages quoted in a review, no part of this book
may be reproduced in any form, by photostat, microfilm,
xerography, or any other means, or incorporated into any
information retrieval system, electronic or mechanical, without
the written permission of the copyright owners.

ISBN 1-879691-37-X

Published by
SAN DIEGO STATE UNIVERSITY PRESS

San Diego State University
San Diego, CA 92182

CONTENTS

The University Research Lecture Series

The University Research Lecture series recognizes San Diego State University faculty members for outstanding achievement in research and scholarship and fosters continuation of such accomplishments. Distinguished resident faculty scholars are able to share their knowledge more broadly with the academic community and the community at large through the presentation of all-university graduate colloquia on generic problems of research and graduate education. These colloquia combine open lectures of general interest with smaller seminars and workshops for the graduate students and faculty who are actively pursuing research in areas related to the colloquia topics. The series is sponsored by the Graduate Division and Research and the University Research Council and is supported in part through Instructionally Related Activities Funds. Each academic discipline or department which offers a graduate degree at San Diego State University may nominate resident faculty to participate in the series. Exposure to and interaction with such distinguished researchers is an integral part of the instructional experience for all graduate students at San Diego State University. Each of the lectures in the series will be published to assure its increased availability to the students and faculty of the university and to the community at large. This book, *THE TYRANNY OF DATA*, originated as San Diego State University's tenth University Research Lecture.

Figure 5: GIS technology applied to a small area of northern Kentucky (ARC/INFO Map Book, 1993, p. 107. Credit pending: Northern Kentucky Planning Commission.) A GIS makes it possible to combine, or integrate, layers of digital data from many different sources and to analyze how the different layers of information relate to one another. With the appropriate software, a computer operator can display any combination of data, showing the relationships among variables almost instantly. Combinations of mapped variables can be used to create new maps.

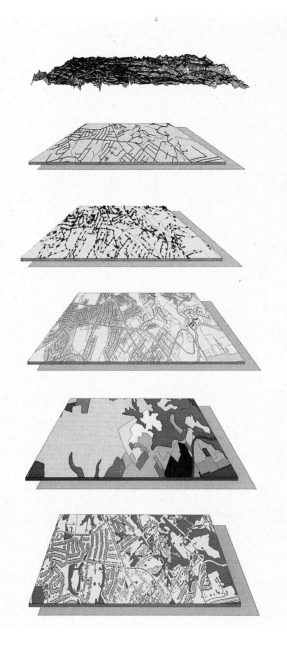

1   *COLLOQUIUM*

Dean Andersen:

Welcome! Welcome to the tenth annual Albert W. Johnson University Research Lecture Colloquium. This occasion provides each of us the opportunity to celebrate, feeling not only our vicarious pleasure for today's guest of honor, but also the direct pleasure of recognizing our own goals and our steps toward their accomplishment. For in creating a public celebration of recognition, we recognize the actuality of accomplishment, and in Arthur's success we find hope that our own goals can reach their accomplishment. We celebrate, not only the person today, but the institution that has had the wisdom to embrace this man into our SDSU community. We celebrate the department which has nourished and sustained his professional accomplishments.We celebrate the SDSU teacher scholar whom we have proudly crafted to symbolize a model of professional excellence, well-suited to our particular educational context. In Arthur's accomplishments, we celebrate what we value, and we stand him on a pedestal, not only so that we can admire, appreciate, and give him the ego gratification and pleasure that these kinds of exhibitory opportunities provide (and also the embarrassment), but also so that we can visualize the statue that we are molding with our own life. His professional accomplishment is our encouragement that we, too, might find the fulfillment, impact, and excellence which we admire in him. We need heroes. They are important motivators, and Arthur Getis is a hero. To tell you about his professional accomplishments, I am going to rely directly on the letter of nomination that Allen Hope and Doug Stow wrote.

To tell you a little bit about Arthur, he currently holds the Stephen and Mary Birch Foundation Endowed Chair of Geographical Studies at San Diego State University. He joined our faculty in 1990, after a distinguished career at Rutgers and at the University of Illinois. For more than 30 years, the thrust of his work has been to understand the manner in which human activities manifest themselves as spatial patterns. At Rutgers he wrote the classic book, *Models of Spatial Processes,* with his student, Barry Boots. The book is still cited as representing fundamental geographical concepts about earth's space, and that book was published in 1978. While at Rutgers, he was known for his seminal work on the nature of point patterns, where the patterns represent objects in earth's space. He wrote a number of articles on urban spatial structure. In addition, he helped to develop the field of spatial location at Rutgers University's Livingston College, and he laid the groundwork for the further development of spatial studies at Princeton University. He spent a year at Bristol University where he worked with the most advanced English researchers in spatial analysis at that time. He spent a semester at Harvard working with Walter Isard, the father of the field of regional science, and in Hawaii's East/West Population Institute.

Professor Getis and his wife, Judith, were the first authors of the National Science Foundation's Post Sputnik High School Geography Project. This work was designed to improve geographic education in America's schools, and from this interest in education has come a great deal of collaborative work with both Judy Getis and Professor Jerome Fellmann at the University of Illinois. This has resulted in publication of a number of college text books including the country's leading introductory book on the subject, *Introduction to Geography,* now in its fourth edition.

Getis left the Chairmanship at Rutgers to head the Department of Geography at the University of Illinois. During those years he wrote a number of articles that contributed significantly to the literature on patterns of spatial association, K-function analysis, and urban research. In addition to theoretical papers on second order analysis, he produced empirical studies of Japanese and American cities. His theoretical work led him to continue his association with Boots with whom he produced another work on pattern analysis. This research was published in the best journals in his field such as *Geographical Analysis, Environmental and Planning, Papers of the Regional Science Association, Transactions of the Institute of British Geographers,* and the *Geographical Review of Japan.* He was asked to join the Board of two research journals: *National Geographic Research* and *Geographical Analysis.* During this period, he spoke at many universities and colleges as a representative of the Association of American Geographers, and to research groups on his work.

At San Diego State University, he first directed the joint Ph.D. program and then moved into the Birch Chair of Geographical Studies. A significant development, at the same time, was the beginning of the fruition of his long association with J. K. Ord, an internationally known statistician. Getis has collaborated with Ord to produce a new family of spatial statistics. These are called local spatial statistics as opposed to the usual global statistics such as Moran's and Geary's autocorrelation statistics. Statistics are used by Getis, and a number of researchers around the world, to study such things as patterns of the diffusion of disease, spatial clustering of economic attributes, and the grouping tendency of land uses when data sets are extremely large. And, at SDSU, he has been heavily influenced by the progressive nature of the department in the area of geographical information systems.He has published a number of papers in this new field, collaborating with a leading spatial econometrician,

Luc Anselin, which bring us new insights into the spatial analytic potential of this technology. He has also collaborated with Michael Goodchild, the leading GIS researcher, on the presentation of GIS materials at workshops around the country.

Getis is one of 11 full members of the 500 person Commission on Mathematical Models of the International Geographical Union. For this organization, he has planned scholarly meetings and engaged in the development of research relationships between members from different parts of the world. In addition he is editor of a new international journal, *Geographical Systems*, together with Dr. B. MacMillan of Oxford University and Professor M. Fischer of Vienna. The new journal emphasizes research at the intersection of information, decision, analysis, and theory, in a spatial systems environment. By taking all this responsibility, Getis remains on the cutting edge of new developments in this fast-moving, technologically based field.

The only thing Allen and Doug left out of their letter is what a magnificent human being Arthur is—a dedicated teacher, admired by his students, a committed professional, respected by his colleagues, a warm, kind, and sensitive human being. Being a nice person is not one of the criteria for this award, but, in returning to my opening, when we stand someone on a pedestal, many of us find it particularly inspiring to recognize that good human beings, good scholars, good researchers, good teachers, good dedicated professionals devoted to making a positive impact in the world are often bound together in the same person. Thank you, Arthur, for accepting the Albert W. Johnson University Research Lectureship and allowing us this opportunity to celebrate you and your accomplishments.

Arthur Getis:

Thank you, Dean Andersen. I am humbled by what you have said—flattered and appreciative of my colleagues in the department who put my name forward for this award. It is strange to listen to a recounting of a number of events in one's life. I realize that I am not as young as I once was. I feel that it might be a good time for me to reminisce a bit (without boring you terribly) about some of the things that I've noticed with regard to the field of quantitative analysis in geography over the last 40 or so years. I thought I would reflect on that during this presentation and save more formal comments for later in the afternoon.

Arthur Getis (written after the colloquium):

My comments were based on a recent article of mine that appeared in the journal *Urban Geography* (1993, 14, 6, pp. 517-25). The article reflects my assessment of the steps that have led to the current status of quantitative methods in geography in American universities. Since my talk was informal and filled with overheads displaying diagrams and copies of covers of books and monographs, I decided it would be better and more comprehensible if the article were reprinted here. The editor of *Urban Geography*, James O. Wheeler, has graciously given permission to reprint the article.

Scholarship, Leadership, and Quantitative Methods[1]

Abstract: This paper explores the supposition that quantitative geography, broadly defined, is the key to the survival of geography as a discipline. Thirteen events of the last 40 years are identified that have laid the groundwork for the success of a number of strong geography departments. These include some of the activities that occurred at the University of Washington, Northwestern University, Bristol University, the University of Iowa, Ohio State University, the National Science Foundation, and the University of California, Santa Barbara. The elements that I find to be crucial for the development of successful departments of geography are: scholars who can mix easily with colleagues in such disciplines as economics, computer science, statistics, and geology; department chairs who commit themselves to high quality quantitative research; and leaders willing to use their energy to recruit high quality faculty.

In this paper I explore the supposition that quantitative geography is the key to the survival of geography as a discipline. On too many occasions geography has been attacked as being less than central to the needs of the university. It is my contention that were it not for the work of the quantitative geographers of the last 40 years, the discipline would long since have been eliminated from or greatly downsized in the research universities of our country. For the purposes of this paper I will take quantitative to mean spatial analysis and theory, the work of the modelers, both human and physical, the economic geographic theorists and spatial econometricians, the spatial statisticians, those cartographers and remote sensers who attempt to use the latest technologies to improve maps and data visualization for analytical purposes, and the geographic information specialists who develop new technologies, new software, and new ways of analyzing geographic problems.

This seeming self congratulation should not be misinterpreted. I am not saying that quantitative geography is more academically valid than the other areas of the discipline. I am saying, however, that the quantitative researchers have been largely responsible for bringing the resources and broad recognition to their departments that allow for the existence of graduate programs. As we all know, graduate programs are the lifeblood of research universities.

I am not able to prove my point unequivocally, simply because samples are too small and hard data elusive. In fact, relatively few departments have been eliminated or disbanded in the last 50 years. Also, one can argue that only a few departments can be considered strongly quantitative in emphasis. In this paper, however, I will identify a series of events that I believe solidified the place of geography in research universities. None of the events has led to an expansion of the discipline beyond what might be expected given the increase in the size of our universities. In addition, none of the events has led to the reentry of geography as a discipline into the Ivy League. When and if geography is reestablished at Ivy League universities, I think it will be because quantitative geography will have made sufficient strides to catch the attention of a suitable number of non-geographic scholars at those universities.

The road to 1993 has been bumpy. Geography has lost strength in some universities and gained in others. The departments that have shone in the late 1980s and early 1990s are mainly those that have adopted new computer technology, developed models using high-level software, and emphasized geographic information systems. Any summary of the listings in *Jobs in Geography* clearly indicates that the demand for quantitative geographers is persistently greater than that for other emphases.

Traditionally, the leaders in strong geography departments insure that new trends are given at least lip-service; they usually have at least one or two quantitative geographers on their staffs and several related faculty whose job it is to bring in money to support graduate students. For all practical purposes, those leaders who failed to follow even that minimalist strategy have been forced to downsize or wait for the university to divest them. Only a few departments survive without insuring that the quantitative area is well-covered. As in many samples, these are the anomalous observations that are based on factors deeply ingrained in the history of geography before the quantitative interest grew.

There has always been a distrust of if not contempt for quantification in geography. Sometimes the feeling is based on philosophy, sometimes jealousy, and sometimes ignorance. Most departments fail to commit themselves wholeheartedly to the work of the quantifiers, even though most benefit from their existence. The lack of commitment comes from fundamental attitudes about the manipulation of numbers, symbols, and computer technology. Many of those who are attracted to the discipline seek a pleasant refuge away from fields of study that require quantitative skills. Thus, our professional field has been in an uneasy alliance between those who are most responsible for the existence of graduate programs and those who find that numbers and models detract from what they might call "the essence" of the discipline.

Not long ago I heard a colleague say that so-and-so at x university, a quantitative geographer, is a poor faculty member because he spends so little time with students and talks to only a few people, mainly from outside the department. My friend had to admit, however, that the so-and-so is directly and indirectly responsible for many departmental successes simply because his work is well-known, highly respected, and on the cutting edge of quantitative research. The department might be happier without him, but then again, the department might not be there if he weren't there.

The departments and programs that house well-known modelers and benefit from the flow of research money directly or indirectly owe their success to the events of the past that paved the way for the strong research programs of today. I have listed 13 events of the last 40 years that have laid the groundwork for the success of a fairly large number of strong geography departments. This is my personal view, based on my own experiences. I make no claim that it is an exhaustive list; my original list was longer, but space limits me. I know that it slights the importance of the Canadian geographers who have labored long and successfully in the quantitative field. Others could well come up with a completely different set of events, based on their own vantage point.

I. THE INTEREST IN TECHNOLOGY AND STATISTICS AT WASHINGTON

This is the 40th anniversary year of the publication in the *Annals of the AAG* of Fred K. Schaefer's article on "exceptionalism" in geography. Schaefer extolled the virtues of geography as a science of earth space and denigrated the idiographic approach of Hartshorne and his followers. Although his article was widely read at the University of Washington in the late 1950s, it was not to Iowa's Schaefer that one must attribute the new focus on quantitative methods in geography. To my mind, the unquestioned leader of a radically new approach to quantitative methods in geography was William Garrison.

He was and is interested in new technology and the latest operations theory that enables transportation systems and spatial interaction to operate effectively. [Figures 1-3 graphically depict the theoretical underpinnings on which the quantitative work was based.] This interest led to the need to learn about statistics, modeling, and economic theory. These were and are the very ingredients on which many public agencies spend millions for research expertise. Unlike most geographers of his time at Washington, William Garrison knew that one must go beyond the boundaries of the department and the university to forge the contacts that allow for strong research programs. Not all of the students at Washington followed Garrison's path, but many of them—Brian Berry, Duane Marble, Richard Morrill, John Nystuen, Michael Dacey, Herman Porter, William Bunge, Ronald Boyce, and Waldo Tobler—influenced by Garrison's need to be on the frontier, became the quantitative methods research leaders of the discipline. Two interesting sidelights: some of these students came to Washington to study under Edward Ullman but found the intensity of Garrison's intellectualism compelling; and Torsten Hägerstrand, the great Swedish geographer, visited Washington as a lecturer in 1960. He influenced and was influenced by the excitement there at that time.

Figure 1: Weber's Locational Triangle

The classical model of industrial location theory, the least-cost theory, is based on the work of Alfred Weber (1868-1958). It explains the optimum location of a manufacturing establishment in terms of the minimization of three basic expenses: relative transport costs, labor costs, and agglomeration costs. Agglomertaion refers to the clustering of productive activities and people for mutual advantage. The problem in the diagram is to identify the location of the industrial plant P that minimizes the total transportation costs necessary for sending raw materials S1 and S2 to it and sending the finished product to the market M. The solution to problems such as this help students to understand how various industries choose their locations and how industrial districts evolve.

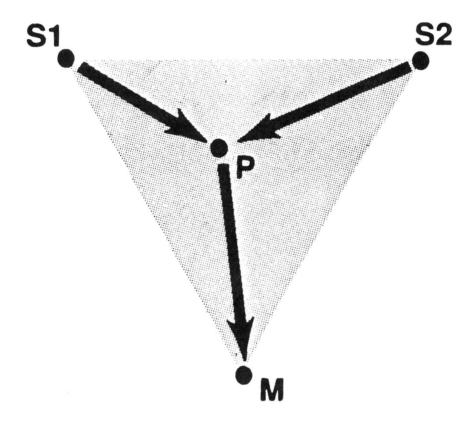

Figure 2: Von Thünen's Transport Gradients

Johann Heinrich von Thünen (1783-1850) developed a model of agricultural location early in the 19th century. Around each major urban market center, he noted, there developed a set of concentric rings of different farm products; the most intensively produced crops are found close to the market; the less intensively produced commodities are located at more distant points. Geographers in the 20th century have taken von Thünen's formal model and used it successfully to understand the spatial patterning of farm land. Since farmers attempt to maximize their land rent, the diagram shows the crop grown on a particular farm is a function not only of market price and costs, but of the costs of transporting the crop to its market.

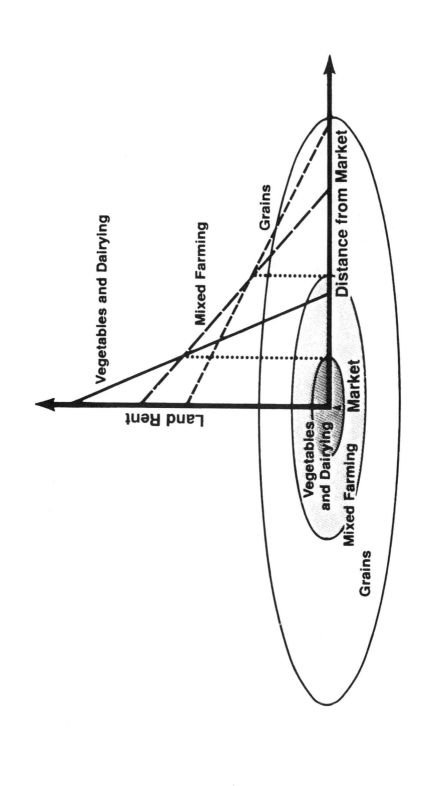

Figure 3: Christaller's Central Place Theory

One of the most widely used models of geographers is that proposed by the German geographer, Walter Christaller, in 1933. It was introduced to American audiences in 1941 by Edward Ullman of the University of Washington. The approximate population size and location of towns and villages (central places) can be explained by the recognition that the services rendered in places of type A, B, and C are part of an interrelated system that is based on the underlying density of population, the minimum demand required for each service to be rendered, and the distance consumers must travel to obtain the available services. The two A central places are the largest on this diagram of one of Christaller's models. The B central places offer fewer goods and services for sale and serve only the areas of the intermediate-sized hexagons. The many C central places, which are considerably smaller and more closely spaced, serve still smaller market areas. The goods offered in the C places are also offered in the A and B places, but the latter offer considerably more and more specialized goods. Notice that the places of the same size are equally spaced.

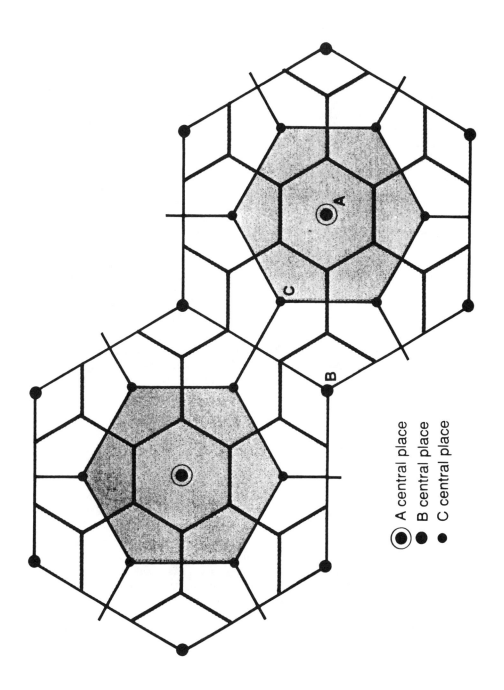

- ⊙ A central place
- ● B central place
- • C central place

II. THE ACTIONS OF DONALD HUDSON

The chair of the Department of Geography in the days of Garrison and Edward Ullman was G. Donald Hudson, a respected Midwestern geographer who had been the President of the AAG and who had strong ties to his Ph.D. department at the University of Chicago and to Northwestern University. Hudson was aware that Garrison and his students were developing a first rate research center. Not only did he promote the statistical work by using his managerial skills to attract outstanding students to Washington, but he helped to diffuse it. Hudson always believed that the strength of American geography was in the Midwest, especially in the Big Ten schools and Chicago. With Washington so far from what he believed was the center of geographical intellectual activity and so different from the Berkeley dominated departments to the South, Hudson made it his business to try to place his students in the Midwestern research universities. He believed that this would be an effective strategy that would alert the heartland to the worth of the Washington program. The people of Seattle at that time, Donald Hudson among them, suffered from an inferiority complex that comes from being remote. He was driven to prove the worth of Washington in the arena that he thought was most important. By phone calls, letters, and telegrams (he especially enjoyed the power of telegrams), and aided by the pre-degree publication records of the grad students, he was able to interest such universities as Chicago, Northwestern, Michigan, Michigan State, Illinois, and Iowa in UW students as potential faculty members. This was quite an achievement, especially since none of those universities looked to the west coast for leadership. This diffusion of quantitative geography caused a veritable revolution in geographic thought at that time. The late 1950s and early 1960s was a golden age for the development of spatial analysis in geography.

III. THE DISCUSSION PAPERS

In the early years of the quantitative excitement, the editors of geography journals did not encourage quantitative work. Stories circulated among the young quantitative geographers about the poor treatment they received at the hands of certain editors of major journals. Quantitative-oriented discussion papers, popular at the University of Washington, were now being disseminated from a number of institutions. Perhaps the best known discussion paper series was that edited by John Nystuen at the University of Michigan. These were the working papers of the Michigan Inter-University Community of Mathematical Geographers (MICMAG). Geography departments at Michigan State, Michigan, and Wayne State participated. The map that represented the logo for the discussion papers was a specially constructed projection by Waldo Tobler that was centered on the small town of Brighton, about equidistant from the three institutions, and the place where some meetings of MICMAG were held. The papers attracted contributors from other universities and Sweden and brought William Warntz, a quantifier laboring alone at the American Geographical Society, into the ever-widening network of geography reformers. As attitudes changed in the discipline, these discussion papers set the stage for radical departures in the contents of some of the leading geography journals.

IV. THE NDEA INSTITUTES AT NORTHWESTERN

Under enormous pressure to upgrade science education in the United States due to the Soviet Union's Sputnik success, various government programs were designed to move the United States forward quickly. The Kennedy/early-Johnson presidencies were years of public spending on the country's educational infrastructure, such as the National Science Foundation, among other governmental activities. Of particular note was the National Defense Education Act (NDEA), which was designed to stimulate graduate education to reach greater heights. By the time that the NDEA program affected geography, Garrison had left Washington for Northwestern University, and several of his students (Richard Morrill, Duane Marble, and Michael Dacey) had begun teaching there. Evanston became the site for several summers of intense workshops on quantitative methods. Geographers came from many parts of the country and foreign countries to participate in the seminars and workshops. Among them were Peter Haggett and David Harvey of Bristol University in England.

V. THE BRITISH CONNECTION

No one writing in the English language about complex, quantitative, geographic research can do it more clearly than Peter Haggett. The Cambridge-educated Haggett wanted to know first hand of the new direction in American geography. Soon after being encouraged by Brian Berry to attend a regional science seminar at Berkeley and then participating in an NDEA institute at Northwestern, Haggett wrote one of the most influential books ever published in geography. *Locational Analysis in Human Geography* made the work of quantitative geographers accessible to anyone with an analytical bent. He organized the work of the quantifiers, synthesized it, illustrated it, and presented it to the world forcefully and with confidence. Where the book was read in the United States, university administrators outside of geography began to take geography seriously. It was read in those universities where the quantitative bug had crept in. Some places remained completely oblivious to the new trend.

David Harvey also attended an NDEA institute and by the mid-60s had developed a manuscript of great length that comprehensively and favorably addressed the philosophical issues involved in the creation of quantitative research: *Explanation in Geography*. Bristol University became the engine for change in a country that previously had held traditional geography in high regard. From England it was just a matter of time before the excitement of change spread to Australia and New Zealand. Canada, of course, was stimulated from two directions.

VI. THE REGIONAL SCIENCE CONNECTION

In the mid-1950s William Garrison spent a year at the University of Pennsylvania, where he met Walter Isard. Isard, rebelling against a "spaceless" economics profession, wrote *Location and Space-Economy* and founded the Regional Science Association. Isard's book was read in detail in Garrison's courses at Washington. In fact, a new economic geography fashioned by Garrison, Berry, and Morrill soon became one of the major approaches to the field. Isard opened the door wide to geographers, a number of whom responded by working in and around Isard at the University of Pennsylvania, Harvard, and Cornell. Today, geographers such as Geoffrey Hewings, Lay Gibson, David Plane, and Gordon Mulligan are major figures in the various units of the Regional Science Association, an organization that has grown to respected international status. Isard does not consider himself a geographer, but his friendship with economists having a strong spatial predilection served geography well. For example, the well-known economist, Charles Tiebout, first at Northwestern, then at the University of Washington, was a friend, colleague, and teacher of Garrison, Ullman, Isard, and Hewings. It was Isard's influence that helped to create a strong interest in input-output analysis in economic geography. The fact that geographers study the work of the economists von Thünen, Weber, and Losch is mainly due to the influence of Isard.

VII. THE IOWA CRUCIBLE

The tangle of associations that led to the early emphasis on quantitative methods in the Department of Geography at the University of Iowa is difficult to document. Clearly, Harold McCarty was the enthusiastic leader of what he called "the science of distribution." Iowa, especially due to McCarty, had its own traditions, quantitative interests, and issues of concern. Many ideas flourished there, mainly in the area of economic geography, including the importance of pattern for finding critical variables and the centrality of areal association as a key to understanding location. Working around McCarty at Iowa were such scholars as Fred Schaefer, James Lindberg, Edwin Thomas, and Gerard Rushton. McCarty was a strong recruiter of graduate students and faculty. He visited New Zealand twice, first attracting to Iowa Leslie King and then Reginald Golledge. Duane Marble visited Iowa for a semester, and William Bunge went as a faculty member but left after a tumultuous year. All of these people had a strong sense of the scientific method, a commitment to the analysis of spatially-based data, and a certain zeal that carried over to their students and associates.

VIII. THE RISE OF OHIO STATE

Edward J. Taaffe was on the faculty at Northwestern during the quantitative excitement and became one of the ardent learners of the new methodologies. He knew many of the traditional geographers from his participation in an annual summer field camp sponsored by the Big Ten Departments of Geography. A great believer in the value of field work, Taaffe recognized that theoretical constructs, analytical approaches, and rigorous analyses were the vehicles that could upgrade the rather impressionistic methods used by field researchers in the 1960s. When he joined the faculty at Ohio State University as chair of the department, he recast the discipline there by hiring a relatively large cadre of quantitative researchers, many of whom have gone on to be the leaders of quantitative geography. With the crucial assistance of Howard Gautier, a Northwestern graduate, Taaffe was able to make his most influential appointment, that of Leslie King, a New Zealander who received his Ph.D. at Iowa. Over a period of several years King's associates who taught at Canterbury in New Zealand, Reginald Golledge (Ph.D., Iowa), England's John Rayner (Ph.D., Canterbury), and Northwestern's Emilio Casetti and Lawrence Brown (via Iowa) were to become the attractive forces that have been responsible for the Ohio State geography program becoming one of the most successful in the United States. It should be noted that Leslie Curry, who became the leading quantitative geographer in Canada at the University of Toronto, was associated in New Zealand with Golledge, King, and Rayner.

IX. BACK TO BRITAIN

In the mid-60s, Bristol's geography department had as faculty Peter Haggett, Michael Chisholm, David Harvey, Barry Garner, Andrew Cliff, and Allan Frey, among others. There is little wonder that a brilliant economics/operations research lecturer at Bristol, J. Keith Ord, would find intellectual stimulation listening to the geographers discuss their technical problems. From Ord's association with Andrew Cliff came the 1973 groundbreaking treatise *Spatial Autocorrelation*. This book gave geographers their first comprehensive look at the most compelling statistical problem they face. Researchers were offered ways to accurately measure and statistically evaluate the possible geographic associations among regions, large and small, no matter how they were spatially configured. Twenty years after its publication, this landmark book and its 1981 successor are still being discovered and used by economists and statisticians, as well as by those new to spatial analysis in geography.

X. SIMONETT AT SANTA BARBARA

By the 1970s, geography's troubles began. Now that academic administrators knew what constituted a strong department of geography, departments that could not reach that standard or that lost key quantitative faculty members (such as Michigan, Chicago, and Northwestern) were under enormous pressure to convince administrators that their subject was differentiable, sophisticated, and legitimate. A reaction against quantitative methods thinned the ranks of the spatial analysts during the 1970s. Very often, departments turned to their quantitative people or hired quantitative people to make their case in the university. This message was not lost on David Simonett, who returned to the United States from Australia to head the weak Department of Geography at the University of California, Santa Barbara. Simonett knew that in the competitive atmosphere of the University of California, survival required a strong move to scientific rigor. Among his first actions was to bring Reginald Golledge of Ohio State and Waldo Tobler from the University of Michigan to Santa Barbara. In short order he built a strong quantitative program that gained fame not only because of the star geographers on its staff, but because the department is patterned after the most successful programs in research universities. The emphasis is on cutting-edge research and high levels of grant-based support from government agencies.

XI. NATIONAL SCIENCE FOUNDATION

Any discussion of leadership in an academic field must recognize that institutional support is a prerequisite for success. Unsupported leaders are not true leaders. Barry Moriarty, who directed the Geography and Regional Science Program of the National Science Foundation, adhered to NSF principles to the letter. That is, among other requirements he and board members such as Waldo Tobler insured that proposals were theoretically sound. Proposals any less than that were given short shrift. As a result, for a period of time in the late 1970s and early 1980s when the quantitative thrust was beginning to flag, at least one leader held geographers to a high standard, a standard which eventually brought considerable recognition from scholars in other disciplines.

XII. THE NATIONAL CENTER FOR GEOGRAPHIC INFORMATION SYSTEMS AND ANALYSIS

David Simonett, as well as many other department heads, recognized the importance of remote sensing and geographic information systems as important areas for technical training for geographers. By the mid-1980s nearly every department had a young faculty member who had an interest in one or the other of these specializations, even though many geographers considered them to be technical and lacking real academic credentials. In 1988, after an enormous effort by the department at Santa Barbara under the direction of David Simonett, UCSB was able to announce that the National Center for Geographic Information Systems and Analysis would be supported by NSF and centered there. Simonett had hired the Cambridge-educated geographer, Michael Goodchild, to head up the center, a key appointment.

Simultaneously, Ross McKinnon, a Northwestern graduate who headed the Department of Geography at SUNY-Buffalo, joined in the effort with Santa Barbara to bring the NCGIA to Buffalo as well. Duane Marble, who had moved to Buffalo from Northwestern, had much to do with the quantitative focus at Buffalo; he and McKinnon helped lay the groundwork for that Department's success. In the running for the NSF institute were other consortia, mainly made up of non-geographic units such as civil engineering and landscape architecture. The fact that the NCGIA came to geography gave the discipline, UCSB, and SUNY-Buffalo an enormous boost. It legitimized geographic information systems as an integral part of the discipline. Today, departments of geography are seeking to develop ever more technologically advanced laboratories in an effort to identify with the great societal interest in GIS.

XIII. SPATIAL ECONOMETRICS MODELERS

One of Simonett's appointments at UCSB was Luc Anselin, a Belgian who studied under Isard at Cornell and served on the planning faculty at Ohio State. Anselin is mainly responsible for one of the latest advances in the quantitative field in the United States, the development of spatial econometrics. This field, which is partly in economics, partly in regional science, and partly in geography, represents one of the contemporary frontier fields. Such geographers as Daniel Griffith of Syracuse and Robert Haining of Sheffield are among the leading practitioners. Parallel to this, Emilio Casetti of Ohio State has developed an entire school of thought based on the econometric theory contained within his expansion method. Anselin's new SpaceStat computer package brings together the fields of spatial econometrics, spatial statistics, spatial graphics, and geographic information systems. It remains to be seen whether this area of interest will make a strong impact on geography.

CONCLUSION

The success of today's research-oriented departments at Ohio State, UCSB, SUNY-Buffalo, Indiana, Iowa, Washington, Minnesota, Illinois, UCLA, Arizona State, Boston, Johns Hopkins, Arizona, San Diego State, Penn State, Tennessee, Clark, Syracuse, Rutgers, South Carolina, Maryland, Georgia, Florida, Wisconsin, Michigan State, Southern California, Virginia Tech, UC Riverside, Colorado, and Utah is due mainly to the recognition of the indispensable role that quantitative methods play in the structure of departmental organization.

In general, three major elements are required for successful departments: scholars who can mix easily with colleagues in economics, geology, statistics, engineering, and computer sciences; department chairs who commit themselves to high quality quantitative research; and leaders willing to exert the enormous effort it takes to recruit high quality faculty and graduate students. In my discourse above, I identified a number of people who knew that quantitative methods are important, acted upon that belief, and rendered their discipline a great service. Today, departmental leaders have the responsibility of passing the torch to the next generation. It might seem like an easy task, but the demands on resources are great and the supply of resources small. All departmental interests, the quantitative among them, battle for every dollar. Perhaps other Hudsons, McCartys, Taaffes, and Simonetts are among us. It is crucial for the survival of the discipline that our departmental leadership seek faculty members with quantitative ability, the highest standards of research expertise, and facility with the new generations of technology as they become available.

Notes

[1] The author would like to thank Brian Berry, Larry Ford, Reginald Golledge, John Rayner, and Gerard Rushton for reading this manuscript and making suggestions for its improvement. The author alone is responsible for its contents.

2 *LECTURE*

President Day:

Good afternoon. I am delighted to welcome you to San Diego State University's tenth Albert W. Johnson University Research Lecture. Before I go on, we are honored with the presence of the person for whom the lecture is named, Vice President Emeritus Johnson.

The University Research Lecture series is a project that is sponsored by the Graduate Division under the auspices of the University Research Council and is supported by instructionally related activities funds. The series was developed for the purpose of annually honoring a resident faculty scholar for outstanding achievement in research and scholarship. Award recipients who are designated "University Research Lecturer" for the academic year deliver a general public lecture and engage in a variety of academic activities throughout the year that are designed to share their research more broadly with the academic community and the community at large. Each academic discipline or department has an opportunity to nominate a faculty member for this award. The faculty committee with representatives from each of the seven colleges makes the final recommendations to the Dean of the Graduate Division in Research. That Dean selects the individual on behalf of the Research Council.

Today, Professor Arthur Getis, who holds a Stephen and Mary Birch Foundation Endowed Chair of Geographical Studies at San Diego State University, will present the tenth University Research Lecture. Through ground-breaking methodological inquiry and significant investigation into important applied geographical problems, he has developed a world-renowned reputation. Exposure to, and interaction with, such a distinguished researcher and scholar provides us an unusual educational opportunity for the entire community. I'm confident that the Albert W. Johnson University Research Lecture, honoring our own faculty, will continue to be an important part of our academic tradition. I would now like to present Dr. James Cobble, Dean of the Graduate Division of Research, who will introduce our honored speaker.

Dean Cobble:

Thank you, President Day. Arthur Getis was born on July 6, 1934, in Philadelphia, Pennsylvania. He was the son of working class parents, Samuel and Sophie Getis, who were struggling to raise three children in the economic aftermath of the Great Depression. Attending the public schools in the area he, like so many others, would not have been able to obtain a university education except for the low fees and tuition of the Pennsylvania State University.

Previously (and at what age the record does not define) young Arthur showed interest in record keeping like baseball statistics, and temperatures, and population data, and, above all, in maps. Not the usual combination of a young man's interests, but Art was not our usual scholar to be. And the exposure to formal classes in geography at the university, whetted by his appetite for scenery, travel, and discovery, apparently were sufficient to bind him to geography as a career and, as we shall see, in some ways to bind geography to Getis.

Seeking an even more exotic location (a weakness of geographers), he attended graduate school at the University of Washington, Seattle, receiving his doctorate and marrying his good friend and fellow geographer, Judith, in 1961.

It was not necessarily a good time to become an academic research geographer. Right after World War II, geography (unlike many other disciplines) was entering both a time of doldrums as well as a period of exciting new gestation. Classical geography was being attacked for not being central to the core of the university. Faculties were spread thin among cultural, historical, international, and economic geography and were facing erosion by the other social sciences such as anthropology and, particularly, from the rapidly growing field of scientific earth sciences. Geography departments were being pushed to find a clear and central reason for existence. Some did, and some did not. Geography departments even disappeared in the ivy league universities, and I well remember a graduate dean and an academic vice-chancellor of two UC campuses some years ago telling me that the field of geography could now be taught by assigning its functions to other more main stream departments—bad judgment.

As educator Getis himself has pointed out, during the last 40 years a growing interest in quantitative geography, the mathematical modeling of the movements of people, and the resulting economic, social, political, and cultural effects, were laying the ground work for the development of quantitative geographic theory. Combined with new technologies in computing and remote sensing, a number of departments of geography began to embrace the new geography and became active centers of teaching and research. These geography departments are alive and well, including our own department at San Diego State University.

Professor Getis has been a leader in this intellectual rebirth. After being on the faculties of Michigan State, Rutgers, and the University of Illinois at Urbana, he was persuaded to join the faculty of San Diego State University in 1990 as a professor—first, as a coordinator of our joint doctoral program in geography with the University of California at Santa Barbara (another distinguished center of geographic research), and, more recently, as the Stephen and Mary Birch Foundation Endowed Chair of Geographical Studies. His research and teaching activities are legend. He and his wife (of 34 years), Judith, have collaborated on a number of projects including text books, and he enjoys both teaching and working with students. Indeed, history shows that his graduate students have gone on to distinguished academic careers themselves. His list of publications and invited lectures takes 12 to 13 pages of single-spaced entries. His research efforts on using statistical models to represent changes in space around us have made him a world authority and an original source in his field.

Still a young man, recognition and honors make up a rapidly growing testimony to his leadership. Listen to some: He was elected as a Rutgers Faculty Fellow; he is one of just 11 full members of the 500 person commission on mathematical models of the International Geographical Union; he has been appointed editor of *Geographical Systems*; he has been an invited lecturer at Princeton and dozens of other distinguished universities here and abroad; he is a member of the editorial board of *National Geographic Research*; he was appointed as an East/West Senior Fellow; he is on the board of directors of the Western Regional Science Association; and on, and on.

His colleagues call him the consummate academician, strongly committed to the ideals of academia, a great teacher/scholar, both in the classroom working with students and being a leader in his profession. His insight and research into the way people interact in the space around them, and developing elegant theories which help predict our future in this regard (for good and for bad) have contributed greatly to the intellectual ferment of an important discipline. It is an achievement that many seek but few achieve and one which this University honors and cherishes. Mr. President, members of the Faculty, students and friends of the University, join me today along with Art's wife, geographer Judith, his oldest daughter, public policy consultant Hilary, his middle daughter, historian Victoria, and his youngest daughter, teacher Anne, and his many friends and colleagues in honoring our tenth Albert W. Johnson University Research Lecturer, Dr. Arthur Getis.

Professor Getis:

Thank you, Dean Cobble. President Day, Dean Andersen, and my colleagues in the Department of Geography and on the Graduate Research Lecture Committee who suggested to the University that I address you. I was surprised, flattered, and humbled to learn that I had been named the tenth Albert W. Johnson lecturer in a University with so many deserving scholars. I am especially pleased to be associated with Albert Johnson, former Vice-President of San Diego State University, a person whom I greatly admire.

I welcome this opportunity to consider an issue that has often affected the validity and utility of some of the best thinking scholars have produced. The issue is constantly before researchers, but there is no uniformity in the way they address it. The issue is simply: Do the data support our point of view?

Perhaps this little story will help to focus on the issue: After constructing dozens of equations and performing thousands of computer simulations using a hard won set of data, one scientist said to his research colleague, "The answer is 2.658395719. Do you think it's right?" His colleague said, "Yes, I'm sure of it because 2.658395719 is my lucky number."

THE NATURE OF DATA

Data come in many different forms. They are the input and output of computers. They are the recorded observations of the writer, scientist, and public official. They are the backbone of our suppositions and conclusions. In the hands of the falsifier, mean-spirited, or gullible, they can become an awesome weapon of control, power, or mayhem.

We draw conclusions from data. If the data are suspect, conclusions are suspect. If the data are accurate, conclusions are more likely to be supportable, but much rests on the quality of the interpretation. Productive and democratic societies thrive on quality data and interpretation. The data come from astute observations, and the interpretations come from well-educated people who have the ability to critically sift and sort data into meaningful statements. The statements are both quantitative and qualitative.

A poster announcing this talk quotes the economist Josiah Stamp's story of a colleague who said about data that, "They collect them, raise them to the *n*th power, take the cube root and prepare wonderful diagrams. But you must never forget that every one of these figures comes in the first instance from the village watchman, who just puts down what he damn well pleases."[1] Cynicism such as this is reinforced by occasional national press reports of unsubstantiated data, questionable interpretations, and misleading conclusions (see Figure 4). In my view, one of the most important roles that a university can play is to have its faculty and students carefully monitor the data and reasoning standards on which important societal decisions are made. But criticism should start at home; at the very least we should scrutinize our own work and instill in our students a respect for solid conclusions based on firm evidence.

Ethical Tremors
in World of Science

Professional community alarmed by reports of dishonesty

Federal Inquiry Finds Misconduct
By a Discoverer of the AIDS Virus

**Rockefeller U. Anxious as Leader
Feels Pain of Science-Fraud Case**

In Commercialized-Science Era, Fraud Thrives

Figure 4: A collage of some recent magazine and newspaper article headlines.

Universities err by placing more emphasis on concepts, theories, suppositions, and conclusions than on the manner in which they are verified. As an example of this oversight, the discipline of statistics and other mainly empirically-based disciplines are accorded a secondary role in many universities. Currently, universities are being overwhelmed with ideas, many of which are embedded in what might be called post-modernist thought, but few of which have been subjected to factual representation or empirical verification. What are the facts behind these ideas? What data support our positions? What process of data manipulation led us to our conclusions? How much attention is given to an evaluation of data quality and to the problems and pitfalls of our research methods?

On January 28, 1986, the space shuttle Challenger exploded soon after its launching, killing seven astronauts and ending a long record of space flight success. According to the Presidential Commission on the Shuttle Challenger Accident, the cause of the explosion was the failure of the rubbery O-rings that are designed to prevent hot gases from leaking through a joint.[2] It was alleged that in at least several instances Morton Thiokol, manufacturer of the solid-fuel booster, rewrote its analytic models to cover the fact that elements of the booster rockets did not meet safety standards that had been required by contract, and that there was a misinterpretation of the data by the managers of the flight at NASA headquarters.[3] Data misinterpretation stands as a potential Achilles heel of what otherwise might be considered good science.

THE TYRANNY OF DATA

In this talk, I will outline some of the problems that are associated with the use of data. I will focus on both traditional problems of data quality and on some of the new problems that have arisen due to the widespread use of new computer technology. Solutions to many of the problems are obvious—that is, more care and attention should be given to the issues involved—but many of the new problems will require for their solution an extra effort. The importance of the issues can be appreciated only if one projects from the results of research to the steps societies take in attempting to solve problems. Questionable research leads to faulty policy, which, in turn, can lead to societal disasters. Consider as examples the research that led to unnecessary radical breast-cancer surgery and other medical and drug debacles, the research that led to the inability of many Japanese buildings and highways to withstand the recent Kobe earthquake, and the research that led, during the cold war, to the overkill in defense expenditures.

The tyranny that threatens the research community is that data exercise a power over us that can lead the naive or dishonorable to misrepresentations. The data may mislead even the most righteous among us. For example, "facts" that are not facts may suggest a path that would not otherwise be taken. A convenient data set may be the wrong data set. A good deal of research effort is often given to overcome the tyranny that is found in the columns and rows that the lay public likes to call statistics.

Scholars covet data. They are usually hard to acquire, difficult to assess, and fall short of giving us the conclusive proof of our suppositions than we would like. For many, our effectiveness as scholars rests on whether we can manipulate data successfully to shed light on issues we consider important. Unfortunately, our own psyches and the day-to-day pressures of the academy lead some to attempt to defeat the tyranny in unethical ways.

Let me briefly outline six problems that cause scholars difficulty.

1. The data quality problem.

How often have you heard someone say that he/she has a good set of data? Good data are reliable; they contain few, if any, mistakes, and can be used with confidence. Usually, a great deal of effort was expended for their collection. For example, quality field measurements are obtained by use of precision instruments, they are recorded carefully, and entered into tables in logical formats. Or many hours must be spent in archives checking and checking again. Good data are expensive. Unfortunately, nearly all data sets are flawed to some degree. To the extent that shortcuts or oversights are characteristic of the data collection process, the research will suffer accordingly.

The Census Bureau goes to unusual lengths to inform users that the data they publish are flawed in a number of important ways. One of those ways is the underrepresentation of minorities in the population.[4] A number of mayors of large American cities, including the largest city, New York, have been moved to sue the government for the undercount.[5] Nonetheless, the data are often used with aplomb by researchers simply because they are official government data and, more important, there is nothing better available. Some researchers avoid the tyranny of poor data quality by overlooking the problems or adjusting the data to suit needs. As a case in point, how often do researchers eliminate outliers without explanation? The solution to the data quality problem is to ask many questions about the collection procedures and to take the necessary steps to avoid having faulty data determine study results.

2. The availability of data problem.

Researchers are often stymied by the fact that the data are proprietary and cannot be released, that data are missing, difficult to obtain, that colleagues are unwilling to share data, or that only a small portion of the area of interest has been sampled.

Someone who is said to have attempted to solve the data availability problem was Dr. Imanishi-Kari, who needed more data to make her case that transplanted genes could stimulate a recipient's immune system to produce antibodies. The 1991 case implicated Professor David Baltimore, a Nobel laureate and eminent biologist. Though she still denies it, the government's Office of Research Integrity concluded that Dr. Imanishi-Kari faked numerous experiments and results.[6]

Professor Baltimore, under whose aegis the work was done, allowed his name to be used on the published article and, for a long time, denied that there was a violation of standard research procedures. The courageous whistle-blower, Dr. Margot O'Toole, suffered job loss and became unemployed for three years.[7] In the end, Dr. Baltimore was humiliated and lost his position as president of the prestigious Rockefeller University.[8]

To think that this type of data fabrication is an isolated case is folly. The problem is much more widespread than most scientists would like to admit. It becomes headlines when the issue or the people involved are well known.

How many of us know of colleagues or students who have falsified data? A recent survey conducted by the American Association for the Advancement of Science indicates that one in four scientists suspects his or her peers of engaging in intellectual fakery.[9] *Science* magazine published in 1994 the results of a study that shows that 43% of students and 50% of faculty members surveyed report direct knowledge of more than one kind of misconduct in their labs, from fabricating results to withholding findings from competitors.[10]

3. The data standards problem.

For many researchers, frustration and disappointment attend the realization that a key phrase or data category has changed definition. For example, the disease AIDS was officially redefined in 1993. While this was done for good reason, the change makes it difficult to compare data taken before 1993 with those gathered later. One solution, of course, is to overlook the change, but then what good is the research?

Another more complex data standards problem concerns the definition of race. Do Americans realize that the racial categories set by the Office of Management and Budget and adopted by the Census are under strong attack by many scientists as being inaccurate and undefinable, and if eliminated from the Census for the year 2000 count, as is being proposed, the effect will be to completely eliminate an enormous number of Federal rules and regulations based on racial categories, including civil rights laws.[11] Yehudi Webster, a sociologist at Cal State, Los Angeles, argues that the use of racial data creates a reality of racial divisions, which then require solutions, such as busing, affirmative action, and multicultural education, all of which are bound to fail, because they heighten the racial awareness that leads to contention.[12]

In addition, those working with Census data know that tract boundaries are often changed. A government sponsored conference is to take place later this year so that we may once again redefine what are metropolitan and nonmetropolitan areas. Such questions as the following are to be considered: What are the basic geographic units for defining areas? Should the definition process follow strictly statistical criteria or allow for local opinion? From these questions it is clear that social and economic researchers face daunting challenges.

4. The data suitability problem.

Suppose that researchers have collected a set of data for a river basin water pollution problem. Halfway through the research, they find that the data are not really suited for the preferred analytical scheme. The question arises whether they need to collect more data or make do with the original set. How often are the time and cost constraints significant enough so that researchers opt to muddle through, saying, "Tomorrow is another day. We'll have an opportunity to gather more data in the future."

In the spatial sciences, geography among them, an issue that has been receiving more and more attention in recent years about the suitability of data is *the problem of spatial scale*. That is, the data are available at, say, the census tract level, but the problem that is being dealt with is at the individual respondent level. In a well known study of congressional election results in Iowa, it was shown that two variables—percentage of the population over 60 and percentage of votes for Republican candidates—correlated both positively and negatively depending on whether data came from individual counties or larger and larger groups of counties, and on which neighboring counties were included in the groups.[13] For the unethical, the solution to this conundrum is to simply select the spatial scale and the configuration of counties that give the desired results.

In geography and in the spatial sciences in general, such as ecology, geology, environmental studies, and regional economics, it is not unusual to see published articles where the researcher uses data available at one geographic scale to come to conclusions about a relationship or process at a finer scale. This "ecological fallacy," as it is known, leads us into a false sense of the power of our techniques and usefulness of our conclusions. The problem of areal unit scale only recently has become generally recognized as a major pitfall in data analysis.

Perhaps the scale problem can be visualized in this way. The problems of the last several years in parts of California—recession, riots, earthquakes, fires, floods, mudslides—are misperceived by the national press. The generalized length of California's coast is comparable to a line from New York to South Carolina. How many things go wrong in that eastern region in the course of a few years? The recession hurt Los Angeles the most, riots were worst in southcentral Los Angeles, earthquakes in northern parts of LA, fires in the forests north and south of LA, flooding in areas surrounding San Francisco and the Santa Barbara area about 300 miles to the south, and mudslides in the fire and flood areas. Nearly every area was affected by one or more of these calamities, but not all areas suffered all of these. Using the word "California" for all of this is like saying that Hurricane Hugo caused considerable damage in the state of New York-New Jersey-Pennsylvania-Delaware-Maryland-Virginia-North Carolina-South Carolina. The scale of analysis is important.

5. The problem of data interpretation.

Researchers at the University of Utah thought they solved the cold fusion problem, but time revealed they had falsified or misinterpreted their data.[14] Think of the fame and fortune that would have come to those researchers if their work stood up to experimental replication. Fame came to Pons and Fleischmann, of course, but not in the manner that they wished. On this issue of interpretation one need only think of the O-ring problem to recognize just how devastating oversights or maliciousness can be.

6. The size of sample problem.

Fortunately, statisticians have developed a battery of tests for *small samples* that help researchers through this dilemma. But it is well known that confidence in test results increases with the size of sample. How easy it is for the immoral to make up data? Frank Close's book, *Too Hot to Handle*, accuses the two cold fusion chemists of "inventing" data.[15]

I would like to pay special attention to *the large sample problem*, which has only recently been identified. The problem is closely tied to some of the technological advances of the latter part of the 20th century. Developments in geographic information systems are good examples of the influence of new technology on the research community. Geographic information systems, commonly called GIS, are software and hardware that take advantage of the ever increasing speed and flexibility of computers. GIS store geo-referenced data in ways that make it convenient to call for and manipulate data, allow for the analysis of data, and prepare the data for output in the form of maps, charts, tables, and graphs. An enormous amount of information can be stored and manipulated. Data on vegetation, soils, utilities, land uses, and land ownership can be separately stored or brought together in layers in various combinations. The data come from censuses, surveys, remotely sensed satellite imagery, government hydrographic and topographic maps, and many other sources. GIS make it possible to bring the diverse data into the same scale representations for study, analysis, planning purposes, decision support, and record keeping. In Figure 5 (see pp. vi-vii), the top layer is terrain in a part of Northern Kentucky. The second layer shows both streeets and drainage. The next layer depicts four different types of utility lines. Beneath that are shown lot ownership lines. Fifth down are various official zones for voting, school districts, census tracts, and zoning. Finally, at the bottom, buildings and some of the features in the layers above are brought together for analysis and decision making.

The Challenge of the New Technology

The development of this technology has made data available in amounts, detail, and in combinations that boggle the mind. College courses in GIS are springing up all over the country to help prepare students for the technological onslaught. Currently, half the cost of GIS implementation, however, is required for converting data from their original sources into a digital-vector form, the preferred data structure. The estimated cost of data conversion in the United States is about $1 billion a year.[16] Conversion tools are being developed to make the job less labor intensive.

A new term, metadata, is used for the detailed description of the origin, size, quality, time, place, and so on, of the large data sets.[17] (See Figure 6)

In the recent past, analysts thought 1,000 observations or so constituted a large data set. Today, it is not unusual to have extensive coverages of parts of the earth where each observation represents a few square meters of earth space. This means that our new data sets may have millions of observations. On a satellite image, each of the tiny picture elements, called pixels, may represent a land cover type for a 10 by 10 meter plot on the earth's surface.

New forms of statistical analysis are needed to assess the relationships between variables. Even new theories have to be devised to attempt to understand relationships among variables at this level of resolution. What is the relationship, for example, between moisture and plant growth when our reference is several square feet of earth space? How do we assess the clustering of cases of malaria when our environmental data are recorded in a GIS in little rectangles two feet across? Perhaps answers to these kinds of questions prompted Bronowski in 1973 to say that:

> Year by year we devise more precise instruments with which to observe nature with more fineness. And when we look at the observations, we are discomforted to see that they are all still fuzzy and we feel uncertain as ever. We seem to be running after a goal which lurches away from us to infinity every time we come within sight of it.[18]

This pessimistic view is countered by the progress being made in developing and testing new hypotheses about physical and human associations, relationships, and processes. The new ability to explore large data sets without commitment to a firm notion of cause and effect opens the door to creative, imaginative work. New ideas are flourishing. New software encourages the exploration and manipulation of variables in many ways and forms. In fact, the generally accepted sequence of steps in testing hypotheses is undergoing radical change.

At one time, only theoretical proofs were deemed acceptable by the academic community, but now the computer enables us to simulate data and look at all possible permutations of them. You may recall that in 1976, mathematicians solved the famous four-color mapping problem by using intensive computer search methods. The researchers proved that it took only four different colors to make any map where each political unit was represented by a single color and that no two contiguous political units were colored similarly. In the discipline of philosophy, a debate is raging on the validity of computer solutions as opposed to strict mathematical proofs.

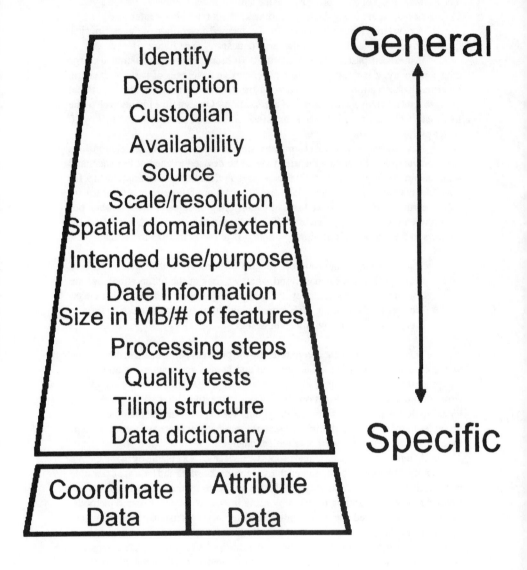

Figure 6: A list of the kinds of information typically contained in a metadata file. (Credit pending: GIS World, Inc.)

The Tyranny of Data Revisited

But yet, the tyranny of data remains with us. The standardization of computer data structures requires that we link data in certain prescribed ways. As our units for analysis represent smaller and smaller parts of the earth, there evolves a great deal of data repetition. Although efficient data storage schemes allow for data compression, we wonder whether the data are being compressed into units that are useful for analysis.

Let me attempt to make clear the type of problem we face. The problem, *spatial dependence*, is one on which I am doing research. Suppose that state data are available for an economic study of the United States. There are 50 observations on each of many variables. California counts as one observation, but so does Rhode Island. Because the area of Rhode Island is so small, there is a high probability that the economic activities of that state "spill over" into the nearby states of Connecticut and Massachusetts, and vice versa. This is much less likely than for a large state such as California. A proper weighting of the data must be devised; otherwise any analysis will be biased. This same type of reasoning is carried into the sphere of large data sets, where very small data units are the rule. Defensible weightings are needed to assess the influence of different parts of the same data set.

The American Statistical Association's Committee on Professional Ethics has developed ethical guidelines for statistical practice.[19] They ask researchers to present findings and interpretations honestly and objectively; avoid deceptive or undocumented statements; disclose any financial or other interests that may affect or appear to affect their professional statements; be prepared to document data sources used in the inquiry; identify known inaccuracies in the data; make clear the steps taken to correct or to refine the data; and explain both the statistical procedures applied to the data and the assumptions required for their application. Perhaps, most important, the guidelines state that data should be made available for analysis by other responsible parties, with appropriate safeguards for privacy concerns.

My hope is that the university takes seriously any breaches in ethical research behavior; that purposeful oversights are treated as serious academic crimes, much as we treat any other kind of falsification, such as plagiarism, and that punishment is meted out where necessary. The stakes are high. Recently, two universities, the University of Utah and the University of California, San Diego, were required to repay the federal government $1.6 million in the case of a scientist who was accused of falsifying information about the immune substances produced by the body when the skin is burned.[20] The humiliation, not to mention the harm to society, is too great to let these problems slide under the rug. One approach to a higher standard is to incorporate into each discipline's undergraduate offerings topics that deal with the way ideas are presented and evaluated, recognizing unsubstantiated assertions, and how researchers, in general, deal with the tyranny of data. It is hoped that this awareness of problems with data will carry over to the public sphere. Do our citizens recognize fear techniques and unfair appeals to bias and emotion? Reasoned evaluation lies at the heart of the democratic process.

At the same time, I hope that the academic as well as the lay community recognizes that working with data is not only a serious business, but it is a complex, difficult endeavor, and that there are thousands upon thousands of researchers who are attempting to follow the most stringent guidelines for data use and analysis. The standards set by the academy have a great deal of influence on the values accepted by the society at large, and we have the grave responsibility of setting a high standard for the generations to come.

Thank you.

QUESTIONS AND ANSWERS

Dean Cobble:

Thank you, Dr. Getis. We've asked Dr. Getis (and he's agreed) to answer questions from the audience. This is your chance to take advantage of it, so go ahead. We appreciate you using the microphone because we do record the proceedings.

Question: Very early in your presentation you made the statement regarding statistics about the number of episodes of misconduct. One thing that you listed was withholding information from competitors. To me this raises a question of what constitutes misconduct and who makes the decisions about misconduct. I'd like to hear your comments on that because I don't think, myself, that withholding information from a competitor is, necessarily, misconduct.

Answer: I think it's a very difficult ethical issue. I think the rules of science say that "the house is open; anyone can come in." Anyone is allowed to see what one is doing, and one should share and share alike. Obviously, there are instances when you are, let's say, working on a problem and are not quite to the point where you want to make your findings known. In that case, I think it would be reasonable to respond openly to colleagues that you are working with such and such kinds of data. I think the game of science (if it is a game at all) is one of openness, and I think that the book, "The Double Helix," gave us some examples of how vicious the in-fighting among scientists can be when one withholds information from someone else who is on the threshold (presumably) of making a great discovery. We are supposed to be scientists who are personally divorced from the work that we are actually dealing with. It is obvious that it is difficult to be open in all cases, but I think good judgment tells us when we can share and when we are in a preliminary stage and are not really ready to share.

Question: There was an interesting article this morning in the *Wall Street Journal* that is relevant to your talk. There was a study that was done two years back, relative to the impact of raising the minimum wage. A health survey, of some magnitude, indicated that the number of people employed increased. However, recently they reviewed that study, went back to the payroll records, and found that the number of people employed didn't go up, but the total number of hours increased.

Answer: Data compilation is a big industry in the United States, both by government and industry. It is not unusual to hear of revisions in the data. For example, just this morning I heard that "no, it wasn't a decline of 3.6% in the number of houses started in December of such-and-such a year, but it's 1.4%," or whatever. Revisions take place all the time, but at least there is the willingness of the various agencies to revise their data. The unfortunate thing is that when we hear the news, as it were, we respond and react nearly immediately, so markets, and scholars, and all the rest of us who deal with data are very much affected by the news and the rumors. Perhaps we should wait until the revisions come in.

Question: You mentioned the issue of increasing volumes of data when you talked about remote sensing sources decreasing [pixel] size. Two possibilities of dealing with that are simply decoupling the bundles of data into smaller bags or perhaps addressing them with parallel processing or other tools. In addition to those types of techniques, can you speak to this conundrum of simply volume and scale and how we manage increasingly large volumes of data?

Answer: I think the challenge is there. If I had the answer to that question, I would be a consultant. But there are a number of people, obviously, who recognize that with the ever increasing technology and with the new satellites that are to be going up in the next five or six years, we are going to be overwhelmed with data. My colleague, Doug Stow, said that millions and millions of bits of information—really, that's an understatement—trillions and trillions of bits of information will be coming to us via satellites. I think that it's our job, not only to learn how to store those data, but also to figure out ways in which we can use them in a meaningful way. We should develop particular kinds of statistics and methods of analysis that help us to reduce this great volume to meaningful numbers.

Question: You mentioned scale and, particularly, with Geographical Information Systems, the collection of data. Is there any way that you can see for an economic incentive to move out bad data once they get into such a system? I know that billions of dollars are spent inserting the data into the system, and frequently, even if the source is noted, the validity of the data or the scale of the data sometimes gets lost once they are inserted, and then there is no economic incentive to clean up the data afterwards. Is the only possible solution to simply rely on things that we can automatically generate over and over again like remote sensing data?

Answer: There are a number of committees, both governmental and academic, that are dealing with the question. I mentioned the term, "metadata." People who are working with data standards, right now, are mostly concerned with the questions of how transferrable data are—not only transferring the data across the super highway of technology but also transferring symbols, objects, and other items from one user to another in a meaningful way. I think that the problem is being addressed. Unfortunately, we are spending a great deal of time in our laboratories (and, therefore, money) cleaning data. In fact, it is not unusual to hear researchers say, after several weeks or several months of hard work, "Yes, the data are clean," but they are exhausted. These kinds of technology related problems are going to be the big issues in the latter part of this decade and into the next.

Dean Cobble:
If there are no more questions, I would like to thank those present. I would like to invite you all to continue the celebration of this interesting, wonderful day for Dr. Getis by being our guest at the reception which will be held in the Faculty Staff Center following this program. Dr. Getis, thanks again for your contributions, being at our University, and working with our students and faculty. We hope that we'll be able to meet the high standards which you've been talking about.

Notes

[1]Anonymous. Quoted in Baron Josiah Stamp, *Some Economic Factors in Modern Life*, 1929.

[2]David E. Sanger, "Virtual Certainty of Failure Shown for Shuttle Seal," *New York Times*, 30 April 1986, 1(I).

[3]Leslie Maitland Werner, "F.B.I. Inquiry Focuses on Rockets for Shuttle," *New York Times*, 17 April 1987, 15(D).

[4]Felicity Barringer, "U.S. Lists Rules for Adjusting Census Count," *New York Times*, 13 March 1990, 25(A).

[5]"New York Might Seek to Reopen Census Suit," *New York Times*, 16 March 1990, 4(B).

[6]Philip J. Hilts, "Crucial Data Were Fabricated in Report Signed by Top Biologist," *New York Times*, 21 March 1991, 1(A).

[7]Philip J. Hilts, "Biologist Who Disputed Study Paid Dearly," *New York Times*, 22 March 1991, 1(A).

[8]"Fraud Undermines Head of Rockefeller U.," *New York Times*, 4 December 1991, 1(B).

[9]William J. Broad, "1 in 4 Scientists in Survey Suspect Fraud by Peers," *New York Times*, 27 March 1992, 16(A).

[10] "Survey Tracks Misconduct, to an Extent," *Science*, 19 November 1993, 25-62.

[11]Lawrence Wright, "One Drop of Blood," *The New Yorker*, v. 70, n. 46 (July 1994): 46-55.

[12]Ibid, p. 54.

[13]S. Openshaw, *The Modifiable Areal Unit Problem* (Norwich: University of East Anglia, 1981).

[14]P.T. Greenland, "The Story of Cold Fusion," *Contemporary Physics*, 35 (May-June 1994): 209.

[15]Frank Close, *Too Hot to Handle* (London: W. H. Allen, 1990).

[16]Ann S. Badillo, "Make vs. Buy - Facing the Data Conversion Dilemma," *GIS World*, 5 (September 1992): 42.

[17]Douglas D. Nebert, "Data Characteristics and Quality: The Importance of Spatial Metadata," *GIS World*, 5 (September 1992): 64.

[18]J. Bronowski, *The Ascent of Man* (London: BBC Publications, 1973), 256.

[19]*The American Statistical Association* (1429 Duke Street, Alexandria, Virginia 22314-3402), "Ethical Guidelines for Statistical Practice," 1995.

[20]Philip J. Hilts, "2 Universities to Pay U.S. 1.6 Million in Research Fraud Case," *New York Times*, 22 July 1993.

3 *LIST OF PUBLICATIONS*

Books

Models of Spatial Processes: An Approach to the Study of Point, Line and Area Patterns. Cambridge: Cambridge University Press (with B. Boots). Reprinted in Russian. (1978)

with J. Getis, and J. D. Fellmann. *Geography* (a systematic geography), Macmillan Company, New York (500 pp.). Revised as *Introduction to Geography* (second edition). Dubuque: W. C. Brown, 1988. Revised third edition, 1990. Revised fourth edition, 1994. (1981)

with J. Getis. *Geography* (a regional geography). Boston: Houghton-Mifflin (576 pp.). (1982)

with J. Getis and J. D. Fellmann. *Human Geography: Landscapes of Human Activities.* New York: Macmillan Company. Revised second edition by J. D. Fellmann, A. Getis, and J. Getis. Dubuque: W. C. Brown, 1990. Revised third edition, 1992. Revised fourth edition, 1995. (1985)

with B. N. Boots. *Point Pattern Analysis.* Newbury Park, Sage Publications. (1987)

with J. Getis, editors. *The United States and Canada: The Land and the People.* Dubuque: W. C. Brown. (1995)

Articles and Chapters in Books

"A Geographical Analysis of Rail Freight Shipments in Pennsylvania," *The Pennsylvania Business Survey*, 51, 16, October, pp. 4-5. (1957)

Getis, A. "The Determination of the Location of Retail Activities with the Use of a Map Transformation," *Economic Geography*, 39, 1, January, pp. 14-22. Reprinted in Bobbs-Merrill Reprint Series in Geography, G-69; Peter Ambrose, *Analytical Human Geography*, American Elsevier Publishing Company (New York), 1969, pp. 204-15. (1963)

"Temporal Land Use Pattern Analysis with the Use of Nearest Neighbor and Quadrat Methods," Discussion Paper No. 1, *Michigan Community for Mathematical Geographers*, 1963, 15 pp. This article was also published in *Annals of the Association of American Geographers*, 54, 3, September 1964, pp. 391-99. (1963)

with J. Getis. "To Understand Urban Environments," *Journal of Geography*, 65, 5, May, pp. 204-5. Reprinted in *Topics in Geography*, No. 1, Urban Geography, National Council for Geographic Education, pp. 2-3. (1966)

with J. Getis. "Christaller's Central Place Theory," *Journal of Geography*, 65, 5, May, pp. 220-26. Reprinted in Fred E. Dohrs and Lawrence M. Sommers. *Economic Geography, Selected Readings*. New York: Thomas Y. Crowell, 1970, pp. 342-50, 1970; *Topics in Geography*, No. 1, Urban Geography. National Council for Geographic Education, pp. 18-24. (1966)

"The Urban Unit of the High School Geography Project," *Journal of Geography*, 65, 5, May, pp. 233-35. Reprinted in *Topics in Geography*, No. 1, Urban Geography, National Council for Geographic Education, pp. 31-32. (1966)

"Occupancy Theory and Map Pattern Analysis." University of Bristol, England: Department of Geography Seminar Series, No. 1, Series A, April, 23 pp. (1967)

"A Method for the Study of Sequences in Geography," *Institute of British Geographers Transactions*, Publication No. 42, December, pp. 87-92. (1967)

"Teaching Urbanism - A Geographic Viewpoint," *Journal of Geography*, 67, 2, April, pp. 206-10. Reprinted in *The Social Sciences and Geographic Education: A Reader*, ed. by John M. Ball, John E. Steinbrink and Joseph P. Stoltman. New York: Wiley & Sons, 1971, pp. 232-37. (1968)

with J. Getis. "Retail Store Spatial Affinities," *Urban Studies*, 5, 3, November, pp. 317-32. Reprinted in *Analysis and Valuation of Retail Locations*, ed. Edwin M. Rams. Reston, Virginia: Reston, pp. 151-65. (1968)

"Some Thoughts on a Negative Binomial Model and Geographic Data," in *Quantitative Methods in Geography: A Symposium*. American Geographical Society, Mimeographed and Offset Publication No. 6, pp. 31-43. (1969)

Getis, A., "Residential Location and the Journey from Work," *Proceedings of the Association of American Geographers,* 1, pp. 55-59. (1969)

"Changing Urban Spatial Patterns," Chapter 4 in *Focus on Geography: Key Concepts and Teaching Strategies*, ed. by Phillip Bacon. Fortieth Yearbook, National Council for the Social Studies, pp. 101-20. (1970)

with B.N. Boots. "Spatial Behavior: Rats and Man," *The Professional Geographer*, 23, 1, January, pp. 11-14. (1971)

with P.H. Jackson. "The Expected Proportion of a Region Polluted by k Sources," *Geographical Analysis*, 3, 3, July, pp. 256-61. (1971)

"Other Revolutionary Paradigms: Comments on Harvey's Paper," *Antipode*, 4, 2, July, pp. 33-36. (1972)

with B. N. Boots and G. Hagevik. "Evaluation of an Air Pollution Intensity Model in the Northeast New Jersey-New York City Area," *Geographical Analysis*, 4, October, pp. 373-91. (1972)

with J. Getis. "Some Current Concepts, Techniques, and Recent Findings in Urban Geography," *Journal of Geography*, 71, 8, November, pp. 483-90. (1972)

with and G. Merk. "Spacing of Human Groups," *Proceedings, Association of American Geographers*, 5, pp. 80-83. (1973)

"Representation of Spatial Point Pattern Processes by Polya Models," in M. Yeates, ed., *Proceedings of the 1972 Meeting of the IGU Commission on Quantitative Geography.* Montreal: McGill-Queens' University Press, pp. 76-100. (1974)

"Pattern in Spatial Analysis," *Northeast Regional Science Review*, 4, pp. 1-5. (1974)

"On the Use of the Term 'Random' in Spatial Analysis," *The Professional Geographer*, 29, 1, pp. 59-61. (1977)

with B.N. Boots. "Probability Model Approach to Map Pattern Analysis," *Progress in Human Geography*, 1, 2, June, pp. 264-86. (1977)

"The Urban Economic Base," in J. D. Eyre, ed. *A Man for All Regions, The Contributions of Edward L. Ullman to Geography.* Chapel Hill: University of North Carolina at Chapel Hill (Department of Geography), pp. 80-91. (1978)

"Pattern Change and Distance Variation in the Square," *Geographical Analysis*, 14, 1, January, pp. 72-78. (1982)

"Second-Order Analysis of Point Patterns: The Case of Chicago as a Multi-Center Urban Region," *The Professional Geographer*, 35, 1, pp. 73-80. (1983)

"Interaction Modeling Using Second-Order Analysis," *Environment and Planning A*, 16, pp. 173-83. (1984)

"A Second-Order Approach to Spatial Autocorrelation," *Ontario Geography*, 25, pp. 67-74. (1985)

"Urban Population Spacing Analysis," *Urban Geography*, 6, 1, pp. 3-13. (1985)

"Energy Costs and Land Use Patterns in Metropolitan Chicago," in B. Checkoway and C. Patton, eds., *Problems of the Metropolitan Midwest*. Urbana: University of Illinois Press. (1985)

"The Economic Health of Municipalities within a Metropolitan Region: The Case of Chicago," *Economic Geography*, 62, 1, pp. 52-73. (1986)

"The Economic Health of American Cities," *Sociology and Social Research*, 70, 4, pp. 298-300. (1986)

"Economic Well-Being Among Chicago's Suburbs," *Illinois Business Review*, 43, 4, August, pp. 9-12. (1986)

with T. Ishimizu. "The Effect of Energy Costs on Land Use Patterns in the Nagoya Metropolitan Region," *Geographical Review of Japan*, 59(Ser. B), 2, pp. 154-62. (1986)

with M. Armstrong and D. Head. "Spatial Autocorrelation: A Comparison of Some Properties of Moran's I and a Second-Order Model," Actes du Symposium 'Analyse de Systemes et Modeles Mathematiques,' *Seminaires et Notes de Recherche*, 28, Cahiers de Geographie de Besancon, 25th IGU, pp. 295-300. (1986)

with J. Franklin. "Second-Order Neighborhood Analysis of Mapped Point Patterns," *Ecology*. (1987)

"Housing in Shanghai: The Chinese Deal with Housing," *Planning and Public Policy*, 13, 3, pp. 1-3. (1987)

"Economic Heterogeneity within Large Metropolitan Areas," *Growth and Change*, 19, 1, pp. 31-42. (1988)

"A Spatial Causal Model of Economic Interdependency among Neighboring Communities," *Environment and Planning A*, 21, pp. 115-20. (1989)

"A Spatial Association Model Approach to the Identification of Spatial Dependence," *Geographical Analysis*, 21, 3, pp. 251-59. (1989)

"Screening for Spatial Dependence in Regression Analysis," *Papers of the Regional Science Association*, 69, pp. 69-81. (1990)

"Spatial Interaction and Spatial Autocorrelation: A Cross-Product Approach," *Environment and Planning A*, 23, pp. 1269-77. (1991)

with J. K. Ord. "The Analysis of Spatial Association by Distance Statistics," *Geographical Analysis*, 24, pp. 189-206. (1992)

with L. Anselin. "Spatial Statistical Analysis and Geographic Information Systems," *The Annals of Regional Science*, 26, pp. 19-33. Also reprinted in M. M. Fischer and P. Nijkamp, eds., *Geographic Information Systems, Spatial Modelling and Policy Evaluation*, Berlin: Springer-Verlag, 1993, pp. 35-49. (1992)

"GIS and Modeling Prerequisites," in Andrew U. Frank and Irene Campari, eds. *Spatial Information Theory: A Theoretical Basis for GIS*. Berlin: Springer-Verlag, pp. 322-40. (1993)

"Scholarship, Leadership, and Quantitative Methods," *Urban Geography*, 14, 6, pp. 517-25. (1993)

"Spatial Dependence and Heterogeneity and Proximal Databases," chapter 6 in Stewart Fotheringham and Peter Rogerson, eds. *Spatial Analysis and GIS*. London: Taylor & Francis, pp. 105-20. (1994)

"Neighborhoods," chapter 10 in Arthur Getis and Judith Getis, eds. *The United States and Canada*. Dubuque: W. C. Brown, pp. 269-96. (1995)

with L. R. Ford. "Cities," chapter 9 in Arthur Getis and Judith Getis, eds. *The United States and Canada*. Dubuque: W. C. Brown, pp. 239-68. (1995)

with J. K. Ord. "Local Spatial Autocorrelation Statistics: Distributional Issues and an Application, *Geographical Analysis*. (1995)

"Spatial Filtering in a Regression Framework: Examples Using Data on Urban Crime, Regional Inequality, and Government Expenditures," chapter 14 in *New Directions in Spatial Econometrics*, L. Anselin and R. Florax, eds. Berlin: Springer-Verlag. (1995)

with J.K. Ord, "Local Spatial Statistics: An Overview," in *Spatial Analysis: Modelling in a GIS Environment*, P. Longley and M. Batty, eds. Cambridge, UK: Geoinformation International. (1995)

Book Reviews

Transport and Urban Land by Lowdon Wingo, Jr., in *The Professional Geographer*, 24, 1, January. (1962)

"A Report on the Work of Leon Lalanne," in *The Professional Geographer*, 14, 3, May, p. 27. (1962)

"La répartition des effectifs scolaires en France" by Marcel Gauthier, in *The Geographical Review*, 54, 4, October. (1964)

Central Places in Southern Germany by Walter Christaller, in *Journal of Geography*, 66, 5, May, p. 276. (1967)

Cities and Space by Lowdon Wingo, Jr. (ed.), in *Journal of Geography*, 67, 1, January. (1968)

Urban Geography by James H. Johnson, in *Journal of Geography*, 67, 8, November, p. 520. (1968)

Automobile Ownership and Residential Density by John B. Lansing and Gary Hendricks, in *Journal of the American Institute of Planners*, 35, 3, May. (1969)

Economic Aspects of Suburban Growth: Studies of the Nassau-Suffolk Planning Region by Dieter K. Zschock, ed. and *The Suburban Apartment Boom: A Case Study of a Land Use Problem* by Max Neutze, in *Journal of Regional Science*, 9, 3, December, pp. 477-79. (1969)

Geographic Perspectives on Urban Systems: With Integrated Readings by Brian J. L. Berry and Frank E. Horton, in *Journal of the American Institute of Planners*, 37, 2, March, p. 134. (1971)

The Merchant's World: The Geography of Wholesaling by James Vance, Jr., in *Economic Geography*, 47, 3, July, p. 461. (1971)

Ecologic-Economic Analysis for Regional Development by Walter Isard, *et al.*, in *Geographical Review*, 63, 4, pp. 586-87. (1973)

Modernizing Urban Land Policy, ed. by Marion Clawson, in *Growth and Change*, 5, 3, p. 47. (1974)

One-Dimensional Central Place Theory by Michael F. Dacey, *et al.*, in *Journal of Regional Science*, 15, 3, pp. 382-83. (1975)

Maps and Statistics by Peter Lewis, in *Annals of the Association of American Geographers*, 68, 4, pp. 582-83. (1978)

Production Systems and Hierarchies of Centres: The Relationship Spatial and Economic Structures by Jan Gunnarsson, in *Regional Perspectives*, 9, 2, p. 132. (1979)

Alone Together: Social Order on an Urban Beach by Robert B. Edgerton, in *Human Ecology*, 8, 4, pp. 417-18. (1980)

Urban Residential Location Models by S. H. Putnam, in *The Professional Geographer*, 32, 4, pp. 498-99. (1980)

Applied Linear Programming by M. R. Greenberg, in *Geographical Review*, 70, 2, pp. 366-67. (1980)

"The Green Revolution Game" by G. Chapman, in *Simulation and Games*, 15, 1, 119-20.
U.S. 40 Today by T. and G. Vale, in *Journal of Geography*. (1985)

The Social Production of Urban Space by M. Gottdiener, in *Geographical Review*. (1986)

Spatial Data Analysis by Example by G. Upton and B. Fingleton, in *The American Cartographer*, pp. 363-65. (1986)

Mathematical Methods in Human Geography and Planning by A. G. Wilson and R. J. Bennett, in *American Scientist*, September. (1987)

The Emergence of Los Angeles by Bernard Marchand, in *Urban Geography*, 9, 2, pp. 221-22. (1987)

Distribution of Distances in Pregeographical Space by H. Kuiper, in *The Professional Geographer*, 40, 3, pp. 358-59. (1988)

Spatial Autocorrelation: A Primer by D. Griffith, in *Economic Geography*, 1, pp. 88-89. (1989)

Spatial Diffusion by R. Morrill, G. L. Gaile, and G. I. Thrall, in *The Annals of Regional Science*, 23, 3, pp. 248-49. (1989)

Advanced Spatial Statistics by D.A. Griffith, in *The Annals of Regional Science*, 25, pp. 226-28. (1991)

Statistics for Spatial Data by Noel Cressie, in *Journal of Regional Science*, 32, 4, pp. 511-13. (1992)

Spatial Tessellations: Concepts and Applications of Voronoi Diagrams, by Atsuyuki Okabe, Barry Boots, and Kokichi Sugihara, in *Geographical Analysis*, 26, 1, pp. 88-90. (1994)

Spatial Econometrics of Services, by A. S. Bailly, W. J. Coffey, J. H. P. Paelinck, and M. Polese, in *Journal of Retailing and Consumer Services*, 1, 2, pp. 116. (1994)